Bumblebee Sweets and a See-Through Stomach

Poems by Brian Patten and Tony Mitton

Contents

Illustrated by Colin Jack and Robert Dunn

A Dog's Life

Sigh, sob, gulp, bark, gush,
I'm soggy, swampy, saturated,
Bath time's something
I've always hated.

I'm bedewed, bedraggled,
Waterlogged,
My ears are frothy,
My dose is clogged.

I might grow fungus!
I might rust!
Bathing a dog
Is most unjust.

Dear Mum,

While you were out
A cup went and broke itself on purpose,
A crack appeared in that blue vase
Your great grandad brought back from
Mr Ming in China.
Somehow, without me even turning on the tap
The sink mysteriously overflowed
And a strange jam stain
(About the size of a boy's hand)
Suddenly appeared on the new sofa.
I don't think we will ever discover
How the cat managed to turn on
the washing machine,
Especially from the inside,
Or how Sis's pet rabbit went and mistook
The waste-disposal unit for a burrow.
Also, I know the canary looks grubby
But it took me ages
Getting it out of the vacuum cleaner.
I was being good (Honest)
But I think the house is haunted
And knowing you're going to have a fit
I've gone over to Gran's
To lie low for a bit.

3

The Day I Got My Finger Stuck up My Nose

When I got my finger stuck up my nose
I went to a doctor, who said,
"Nothing like this has happened before,
We will have to chop off your head."

"It's only my finger stuck up my nose,
It's only my finger!" I said.
"I can see what it is," the doctor replied,
"But we'll still have to chop off your head."

He went to the cabinet. He took out an axe.
I watched with considerable dread.
"But it's only my finger stuck up my nose.
It's only a finger!" I said.

"Perhaps we can yank it out with a hook
Tied to some surgical thread.
Maybe we can try that," he replied,
"Rather than chop off your head."

"I'm never going to pick it again.
I've now learned my lesson," I said.
"I won't stick my finger up my nose –
I'll stick it in my ear instead."

Cousin Lesley's See-through Stomach

Cousin Lesley took a pill
That made her go invisible.
Perhaps this would have been all right
If everything was out of sight.

But all around her stomach swam
 Half-digested bread and jam,
And no matter how she tried
 She couldn't hide what was inside.

In the morning we often noted
How the toast and porridge floated,
And how unappetizing in the light
Was the curry from last night.

Some old cheese had fallen victim
To her strange digestive system,
And there seemed a million ways
To digest old mayonnaise.

We were often fascinated
By the stuff left undigested,
A mish-mash of peas and jelly
Drifted round our cousin's belly.

Certain bits of Cornish pastie
Looked repugnant and quite nasty,
While the strawberries from last year
Were without the cream, I fear.

And at dinner, oh dear me!
What a disgusting sight to see
Chewed-up fish and cold brown tea
Where Cousin Lesley's tum should be.

The Irreplaceable Mum

If you were a crack in the mirror,
If you were a flea on a cat,
If you were a slug in a jug,
I'd still love you. I wouldn't mind that.

If you were a smudge in a picture,
Or an opera singer struck dumb,
If you were a pain in the neck then
You'd still be the very best mum.

If you were a fly in a pizza,
If you were a difficult sum,
Even if you were humpy and grumpy
You'd still be an irreplaceable mum.

Milking a Bumblebee

I tried to milk a bumblebee.
I was only after honey.
It scowled at me and shouted out,
"I DO NOT THINK THAT'S FUNNY!"

Contrary Me

When I was little I wanted to know
Why the years passed so very slow.
Now I'm grown up and as they flash past
I want to know why they don't last.

My Favourite Poem

Chosen by Brian Patten

On the Ning Nang Nong is what is called a
nonsense poem. I think sometimes nonsense
poems are written by poets who think there
is far too much boring sense in the world.

Spike Milligan, who wrote the poem, was a
lovely man and was a friend. He was always
making up funny rhymes and daft words.
And he HATED noise. When he was a child
he lived in India and he went to school in a
large tent on the edge of a desert. Deserts
are wonderfully quiet places and I think this
is why Spike grew up hating noise. When
you think about Spike hating noise so much
then you can see how his nonsense poem
makes sense.

On the Ning Nang Nong

On the Ning Nang Nong
Where the Cows go Bong!
And the Monkeys all say Boo!
There's a Nong Nang Ning
Where the trees go Ping!
And the tea pots Jibber Jabber Joo.
On the Nong Ning Nang
All the mice go Clang!
And you just can't catch 'em when they do!
So it's Ning Nang Nong!
Cows go Bong!
Nong Nang Ning!
Trees go Ping!
Nong Ning Nang!
The mice go Clang!
What a noisy place to belong,
Is the Ning Nang Ning Nang Nong!!

Spike Milligan

Doors

Open the door to the ocean,
open the door to the sky.
The white and the blue are a playground
for you
and your feelings have wings and can fly.

Open the door to the evening,
open the door to the moon,
to the wind in the trees, and the stars, and
the breeze
as they murmur a magical tune.

Open the door to the city,
to the hum of the trucks and the cars,
and the thrill of it all with the buildings
so tall
and the shops and the billboards and bars.

Open the doors of the senses,
to touch and to sound and to sight,
to taste and to smell, oh, there's so much
to tell,
for the world is a dance of delight.

Sweet

Although you are smooth and creamy,
although you are sugary sweet,
although you are wrapped like a present,
although you're delicious to eat,

you're down in the dark of my pocket
as if you're a nugget of treasure.
I'm saving you up for a magical moment,
so as to double the pleasure.

I'm keeping you safe in my pocket,
as I do with the things that I get.
I'm saving you up for a special occasion.
I'm not going to eat you... yet!

Cracker Ring

The cracker burst open —
flash! crack!

Something flew out
as I tumbled back.

There by my foot
was a glittery thing.

Could it be? Yes ...
a little gold ring.

Well, actually plastic,
and coloured golden,

and probably not very
precious or olden.

But perhaps if I wear it
in secret, at night,

a genie will visit.
I think it might.

Listening In Bed

As I listen hard
in bed tonight,

I can hear
the floor creak,
the door squeak,
the tap leak.

I can hear
the dishes clink
down in the kitchen sink.

I can hear
the telly boom
down in the sitting room.

And very near
I can hear
my little brother
breathing deep.

Sssssh...
He's fast asleep.

The Magic Forest

The way to the magic forest
is strange and dark and deep.
To enter the magic forest
you must pass through the gates of sleep.

The sound of the magic forest
is the song of a silver stream.
To hear its tune by the light of the moon
you must pass through the doors of dream.

In the depths of the magic forest
is a pool with a glistening fish.
To stand by the cool of the mystical pool
you must go by the ways of wish.

At the heart of the magic forest
grows a fruit so rich and red,
that to take a bite of its sweet delight
you must go by ways unsaid.

Book

The book itself
is a brand new box.
As you open its lid
your mind unlocks.

And you read that book
by day or night,
for the book is a block
of pure delight.

Then when, in the end,
the book is read,
your eyes may be tired
but your mind feels fed.

So you place that book
on the silent shelf,
but a bit of the book
has become your self.

My Favourite Poem

Chosen by Tony Mitton

Poems are full of ideas. They make pictures in your head when you read or hear them. But they are also made with rhythms and sounds. They are musical. And this poem plays wonderfully with sound and rhythm and rhyme. It has noise that rises to a wildness, but then gradually dies away into sleep and almost silence, like a piece of music. The more you read this poem, the more you admire the writer's skill. This poem cries out to be read aloud. Try it for yourself and see ... or rather, hear.

The Sea

The sea is a hungry dog,
Giant and grey.
He rolls on the beach all day.
With his clashing teeth and shaggy jaws
Hour upon hour he gnaws
The rumbling, tumbling stones,
And 'Bones, bones, bones, bones!'
The giant sea-dog moans,
Licking his greasy paws.

And when the night wind roars
And the moon rocks in the stormy cloud,
He bounds to his feet and snuffs and sniffs,
Shaking his wet sides over the cliffs,
And howls and hollos long and loud.

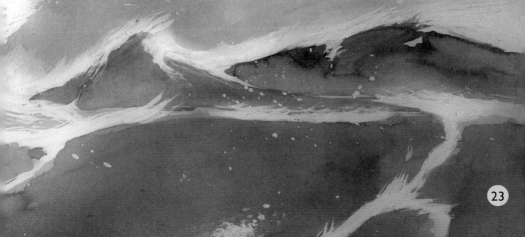

But on quiet days in May or June,
When even the grasses on the dune
Play no more their reedy tune,
With his head between his paws
He lies on the sandy shores,
So quiet, so quiet, he scarcely snores.

James Reeves